play BASS with... RAZORLIGHT

play BASS with... RAZORLIGHT

Wise Publications
part of The Music Sales Group
London / New York / Paris / Sydney / Copenhagen / Berlin / Madrid / Tokyo

Published by

Wise Publications
14-15 Berners Street, London W1T 3LJ, UK

Exclusive Distributors:

Music Sales Limited
Distribution Centre, Newmarket Road,
Bury St Edmunds, Suffolk IP33 3YB, UK

Music Sales Pty Limited
120 Rothschild Avenue,
Rosebery, NSW 2018, Australia

Order No. AM989934
ISBN 978-1-84772-015-3
This book © Copyright 2007 Wise Publications,
a division of Music Sales Limited.

Printed in the EU

www.musicsales.com

Compiled by Nick Crispin
Edited by Tom Farncombe
Music processed by Paul Ewers Music Design

CD recorded, mixed and mastered
by Jonas Persson and John Rose
Additional progamming by Rick Cardinali
All guitars by Arthur Dick
Bass by Tom Farncombe
Drums by Chris Baron

Your Guarantee of Quality

As publishers, we strive to produce every book
to the highest commercial standards.
The music has been freshly engraved and the book has
been carefully designed to minimise awkward page turns
and to make playing from it a real pleasure.
Particular care has been given to specifying acid-free,
neutral-sized paper made from pulps which have not been
elemental chlorine bleached. This pulp is from farmed
sustainable forests and was produced with special regard
for the environment.
Throughout, the printing and binding have been planned
to ensure a sturdy, attractive publication which should
give years of enjoyment.
If your copy fails to meet our high standards,
please inform us and we will gladly replace it.

BASS GUITAR TABLATURE EXPLAINED

The four-line staff of bass tablature graphically represents the bass guitar fingerboard. By placing a number on the appropriate line, the string and fret of any note can be indicated. The number 0 represents an open string. For example:

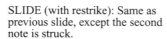

3rd string, 3rd fret   **4th string, open**

SLIDE (not restruck): Strike the first note and then slide the same fret-hand finger up or down to the second note.

HAMMER-ON: Strike the first (lower) note with one finger, then sound the higher note (on the same string) with another finger by fretting it without picking.

BEND (half step): Strike the note and bend up a semi-tone (halfstep).

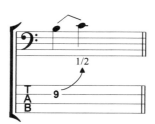

TRILLS: Very rapidly alternate between the notes indicated by continuously hammering on and pulling off.

SLIDE (with restrike): Same as previous slide, except the second note is struck.

PULL-OFF: Place both fingers on the notes to be sounded. Strike the first note and without picking, pull the finger off to sound the second lower note.

BEND & RELEASE: Strike the note and bend up as indicated, then release back to the original note.

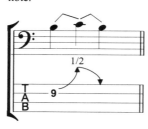

VIBRATO: The string is vibrated by rapidly bending and releasing the note with the fretting hand.

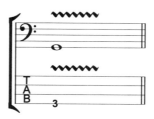

SLIDE: Slide up to the note indicated from a few notes below.

PALM-MUTE: The note is partially muted by the pick hand lightly touching the string(s) just before the bridge.

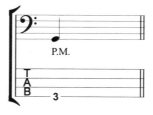

PRE-BEND: Bend the note as indicated then strike it.

NATURAL HARMONIC: Strike the note while the fret-hand lightly touches the string directly over the fret indicated.

SLIDE: Strike the note indicated and slide up an indefinite number of frets.

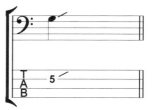

MUFFLED-STRINGS: A percussive sound is produced by laying the left hand across the string(s) without depressing it to the fretboard.

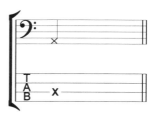

PRE-BEND & RELEASE: Bend the note as indicated. Strike it and release the note back to the original pitch.

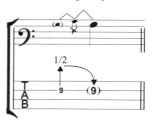

TREMOLO PICKING: The note is picked as rapidly and continuously as possible.

NOTE: The speed of any bend is indicated by the music notation and tempo.

AMERICA

Song by Johnny Borrell & Andy Burrows
Music by Razorlight

Full performance demo: CD track 2
Backing only: CD track 10

Intro
1 bar count in:

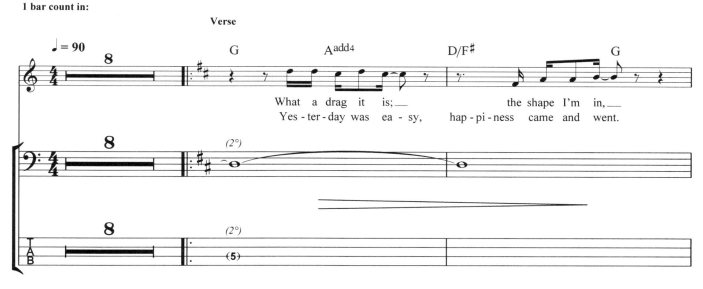

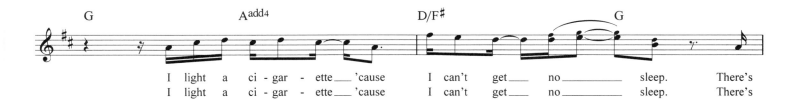

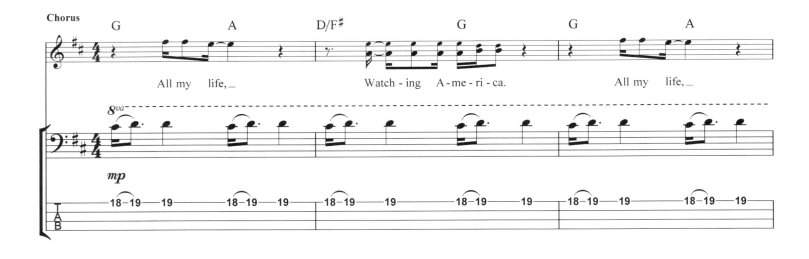

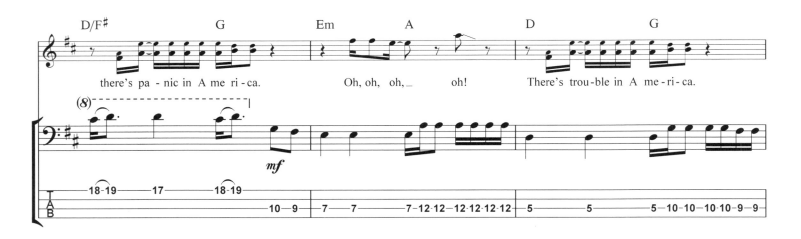

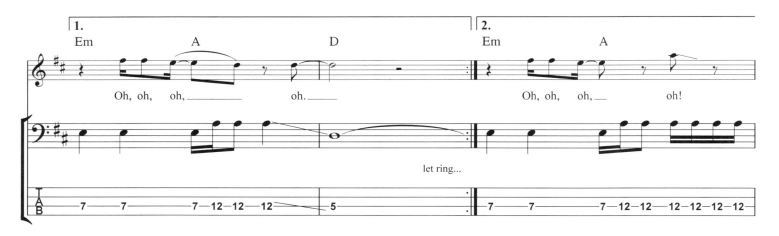

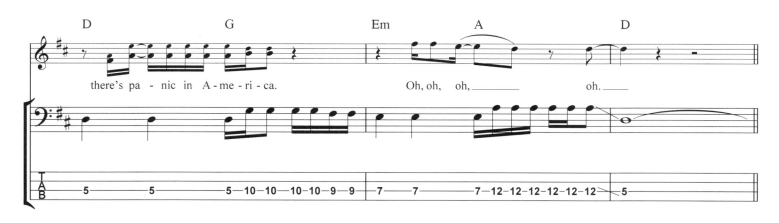

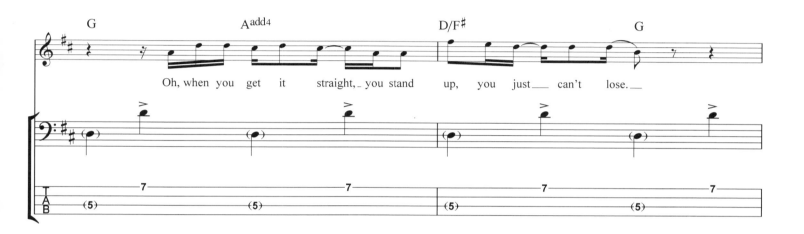

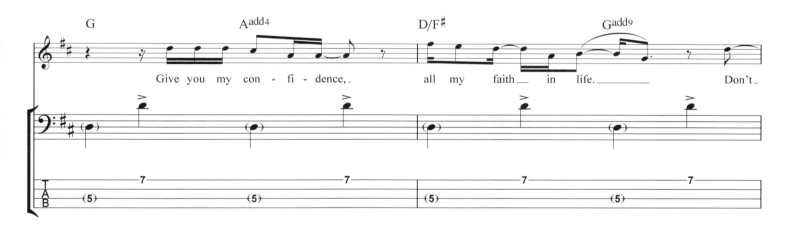

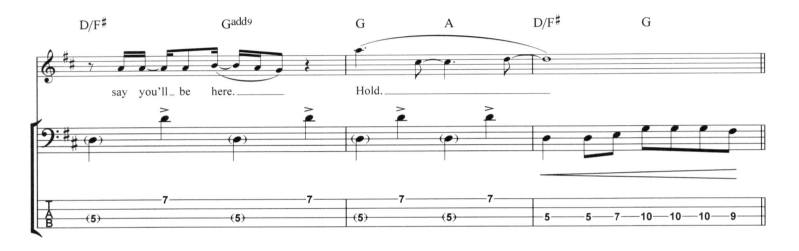

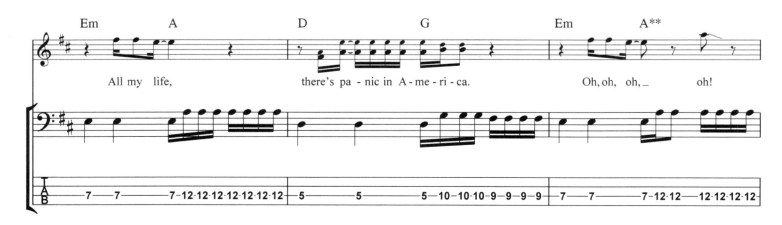

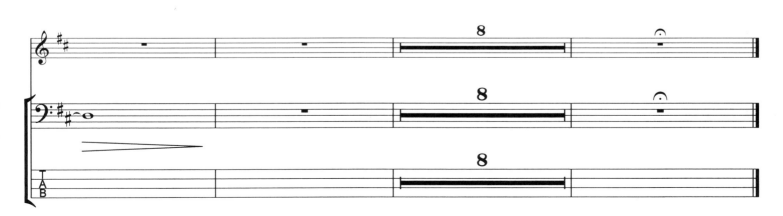

BACK TO THE START

Song by Johnny Borrell
Music by Razorlight

Full performance demo: CD track 3
Backing only: CD track 11

Intro
2 bar count in:

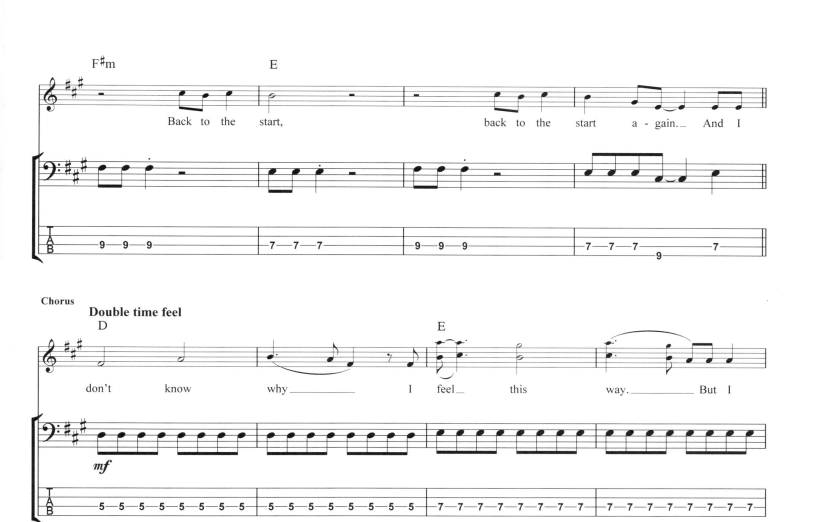

Chorus
Double time feel

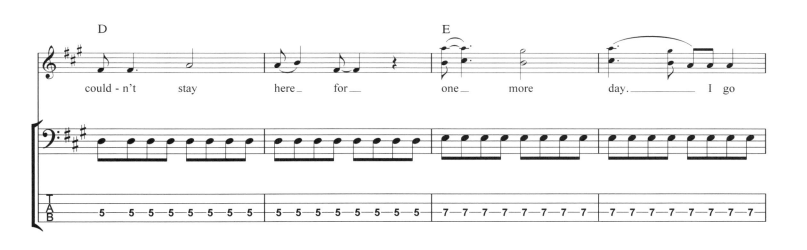

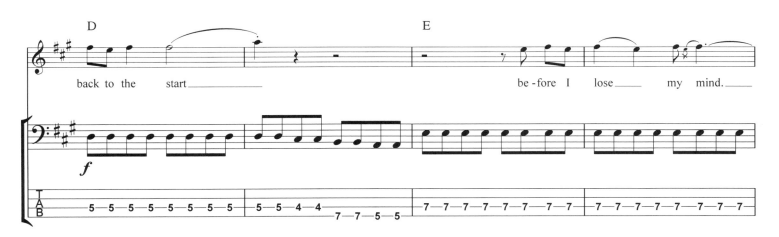

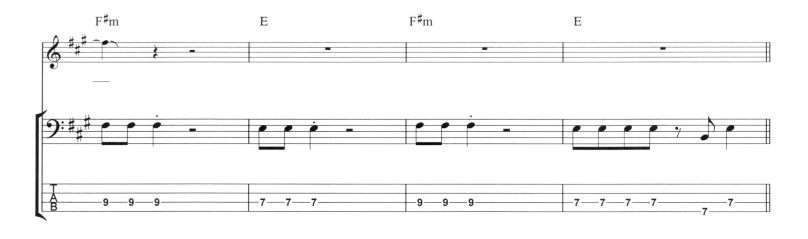

Half time feel

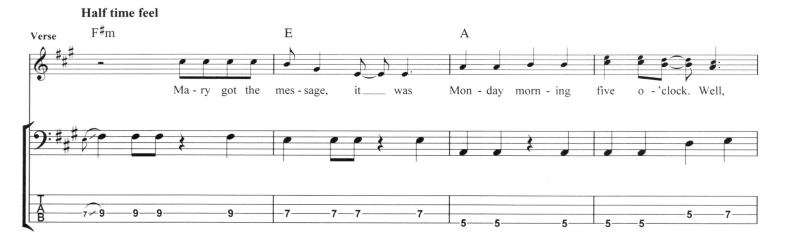

Ma - ry got the mes - sage, it __ was Mon - day morn - ing five o -'clock. Well,

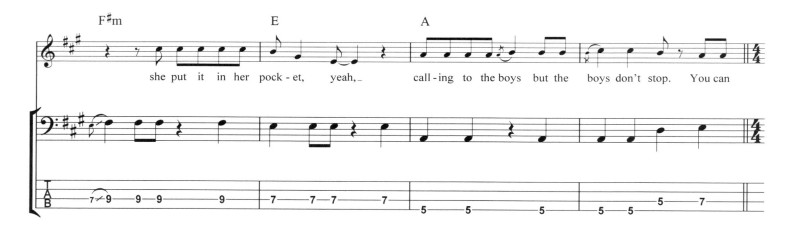

she put it in her pock - et, yeah, __ call - ing to the boys but the boys don't stop. You can

Double time feel

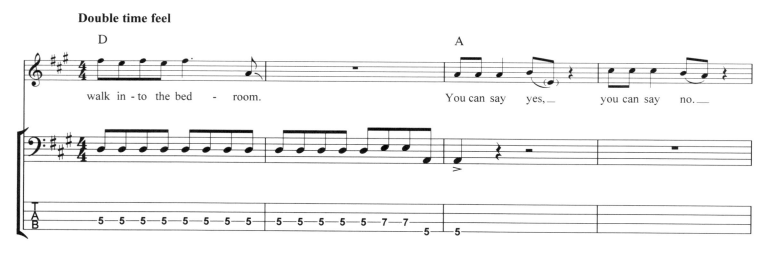

walk in - to the bed - room. You can say yes, __ you can say no. __

could-n't   stay   here___   for___   one___   more   day._____   I go

back to the   start_____   be-fore   I   lose_____   my   mind.____

w/ad lib. vocals

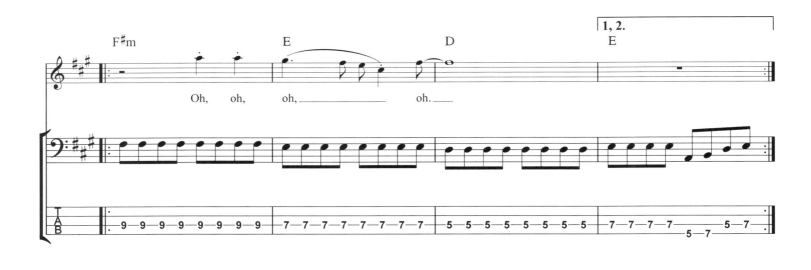

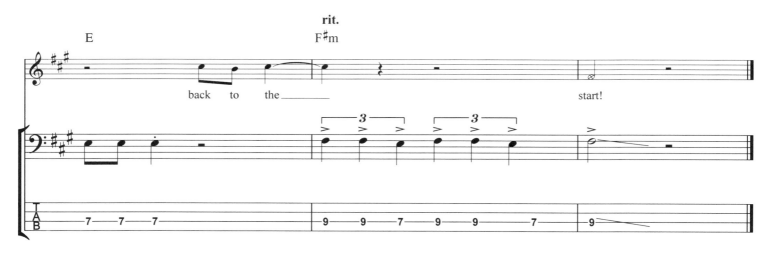

BEFORE I FALL TO PIECES

Song by Johnny Borrell & Andy Burrows
Music by Razorlight

Full performance demo: CD track 4
Backing only: CD track 12

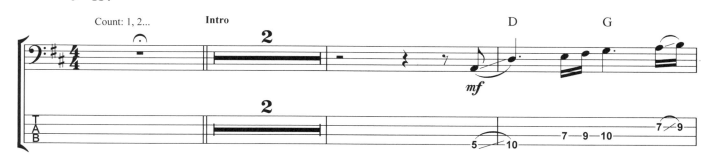

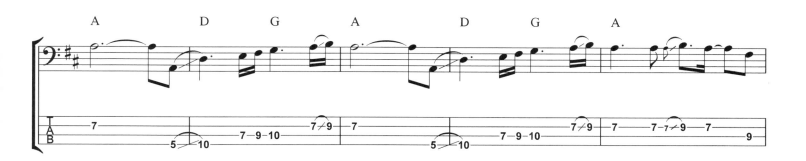

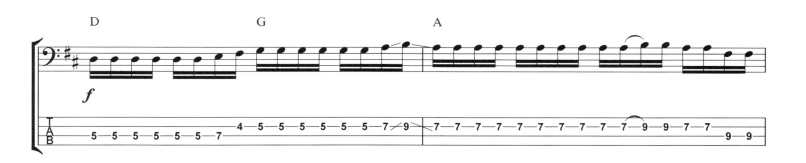

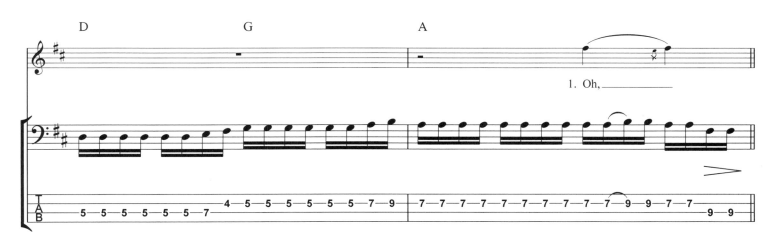

1. Oh,

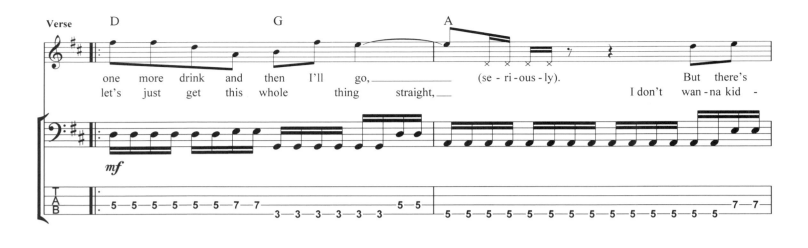

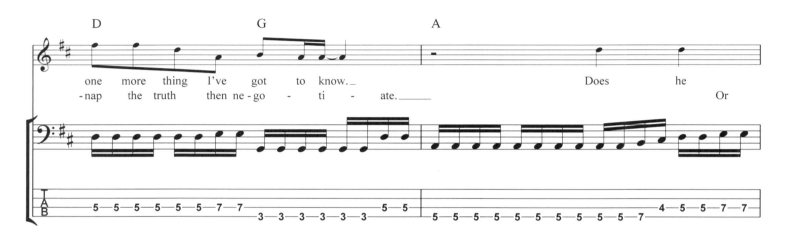

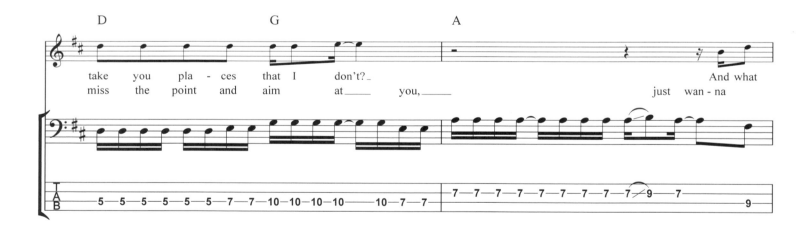

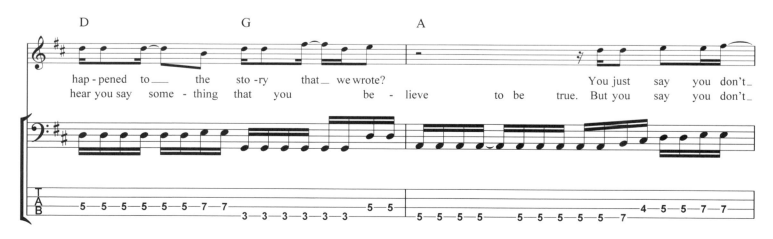

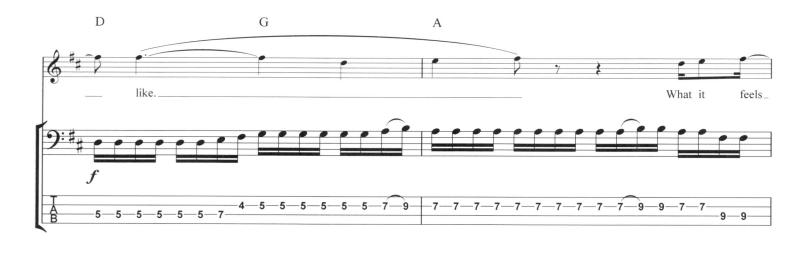

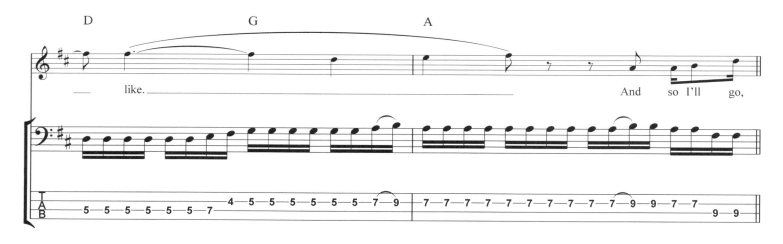

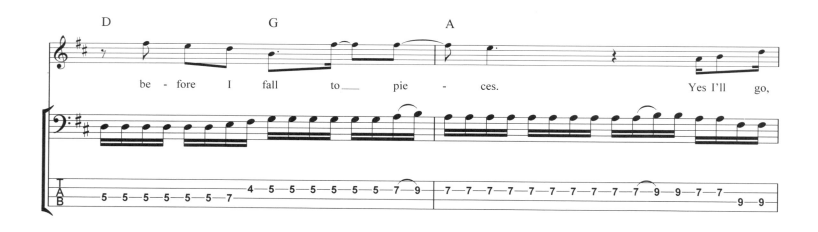

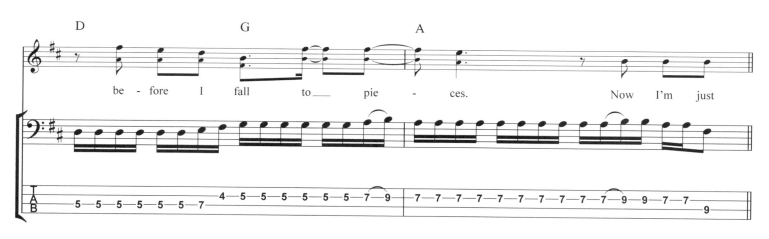

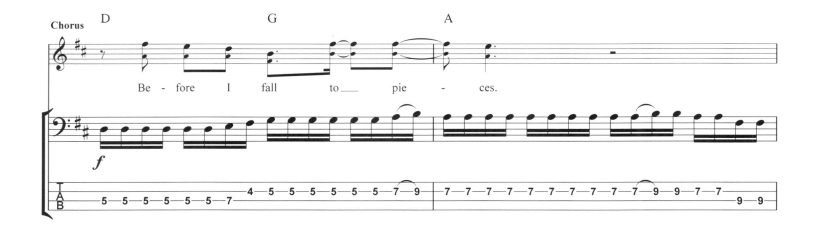

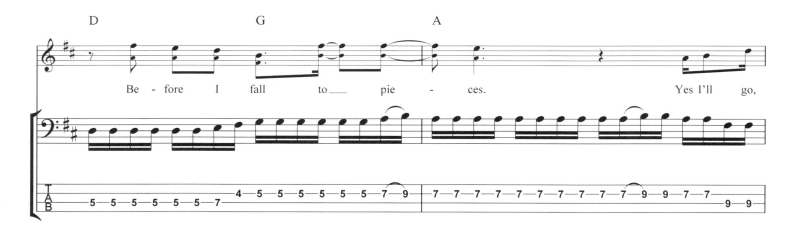

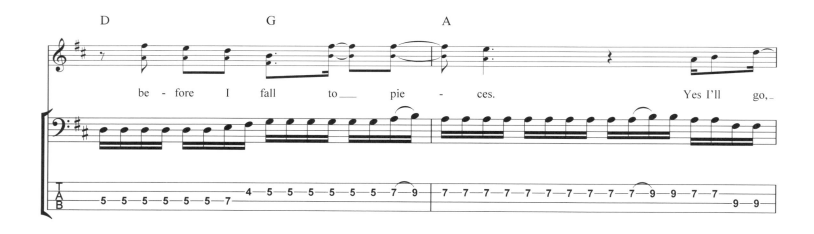

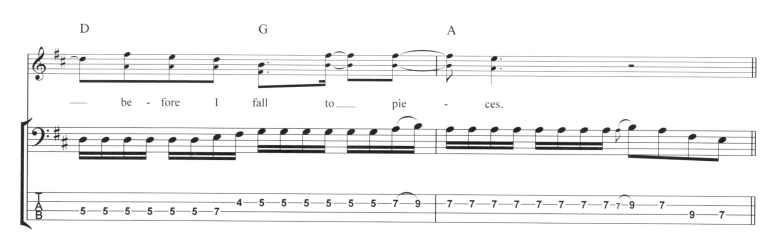

GOLDEN TOUCH

Song by Johnny Borrell
Music by Razorlight

Full performance demo: CD track 5
Backing only: CD track 13

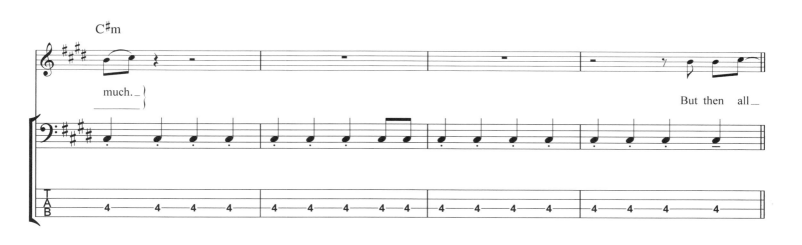

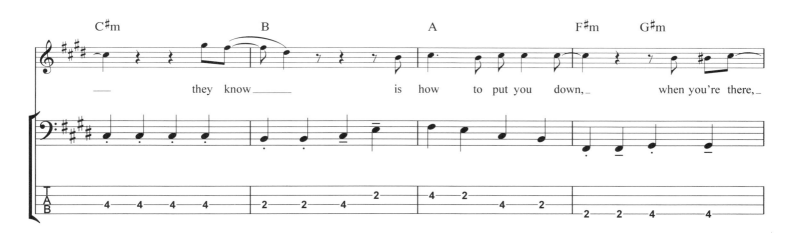

give them a taste but not too much.

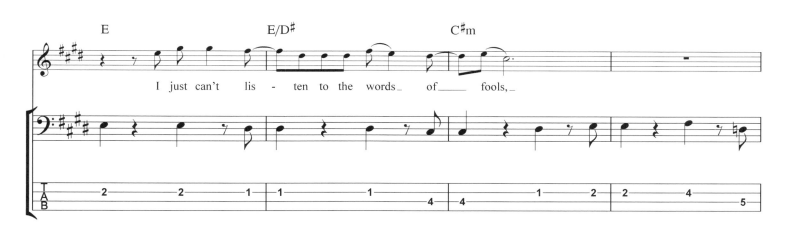

I just can't lis - ten to the words of fools,

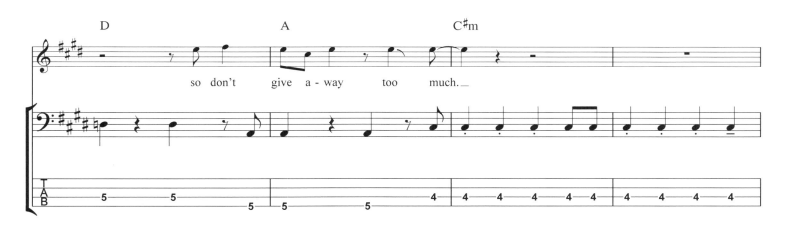

so don't give a - way too much.

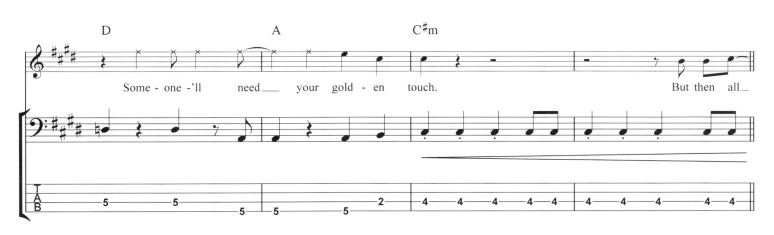

Some - one -'ll need your gold - en touch. But then all

29

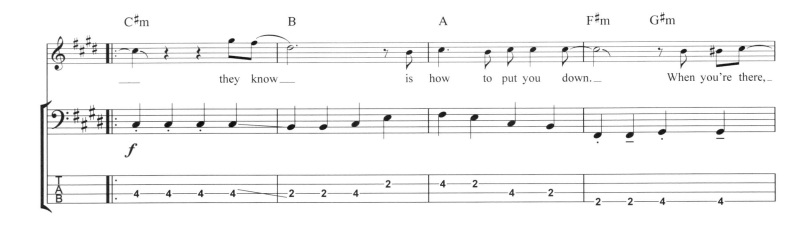

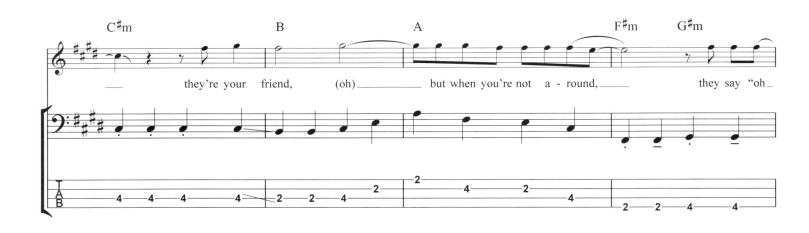

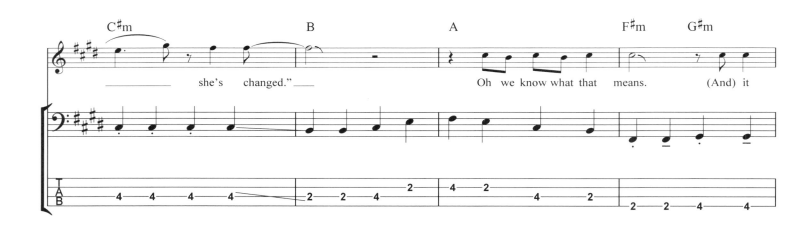

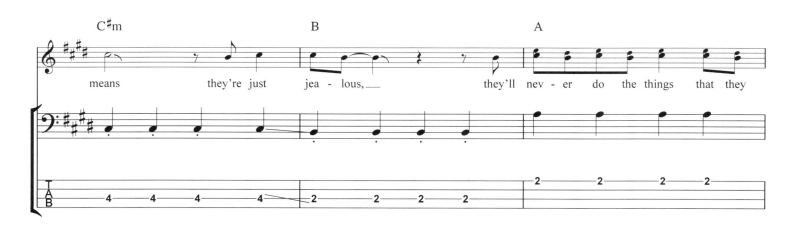

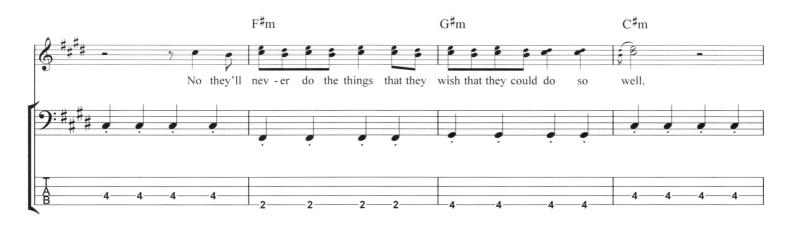

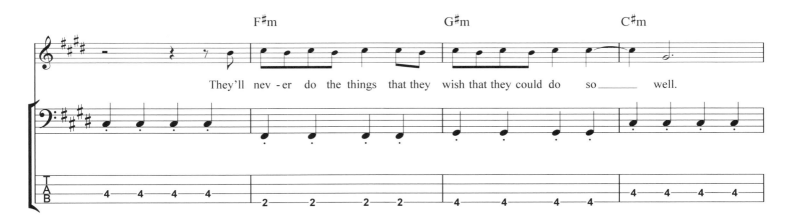

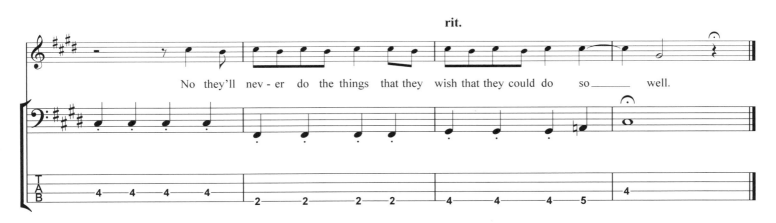

IN THE MORNING

Song by Johnny Borrell
Music by Razorlight

Full performance demo: CD track 6
Backing only: CD track 14

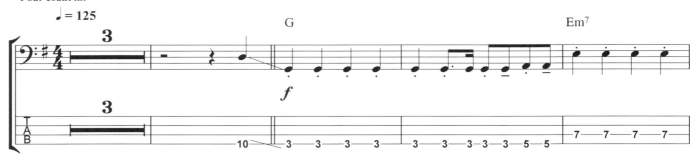

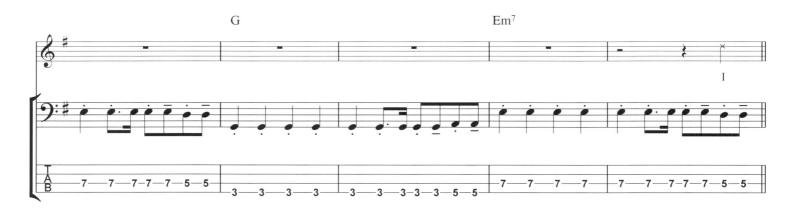

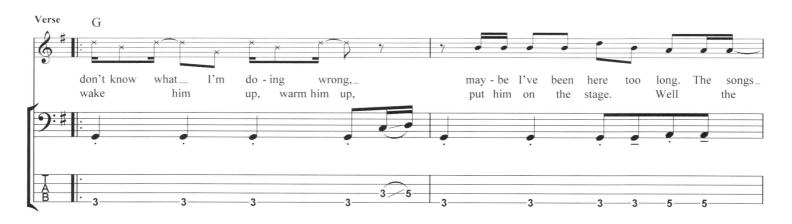

last night was so much fun,___ and now___ your sheets are dir - ty.
ev - 'ry night's still so much fun,___ and you're___ still out there dar - ling.

The streets are dir - ty too___ but you nev - er look back ov - er what you've done.___ Re -
Cling - ing on to the wrong i - deas___ but I nev - er re - gret a - ny - thing I've done.___ Re -

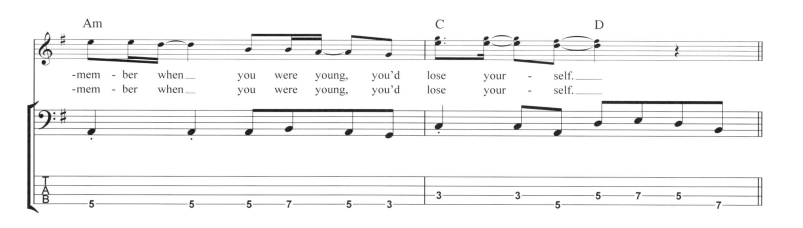

-mem - ber when___ you were young, you'd lose your - self._____
-mem - ber when___ you were young, you'd lose your - self._____

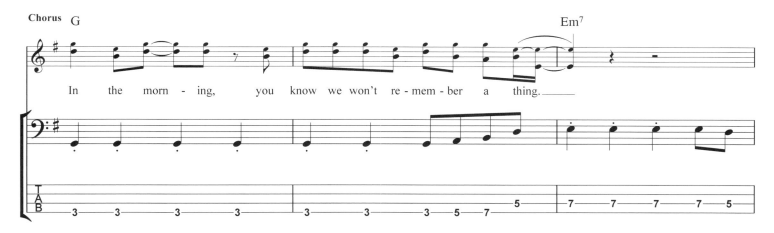

Chorus

In the morn - ing, you know we won't re - mem - ber a thing._____

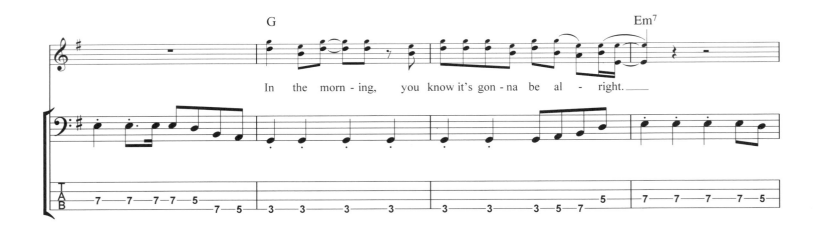

In the morn - ing, you know it's gon - na be al - right.____

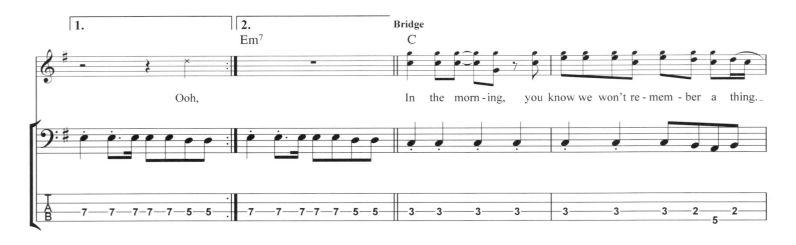

Ooh,

In the morn - ing, you know we won't re - mem - ber a thing.

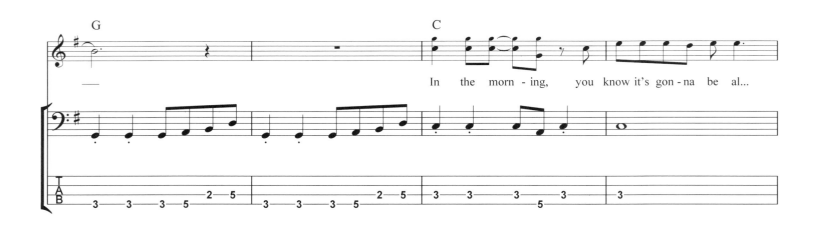

In the morn - ing, you know it's gon - na be al...

Oh.

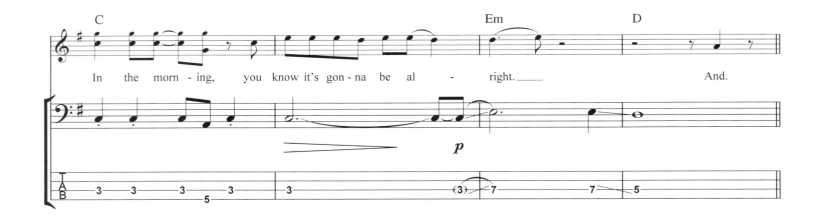

In the morn-ing, you know it's gon-na be al - right. _____ And.

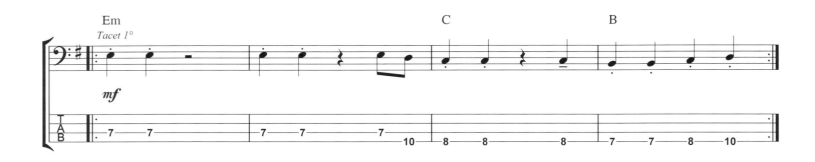

Em   Tacet 1°   C   B

Outro

Em7

Are you real - ly gon-na do it this time?   Are you real - ly gon-na do it this time?

Vocal fig. 1...

C   B

Are you real - ly gon-na do it this time?   Are you real - ly gon-na do it this time?

...Vocal fig. 1 ends

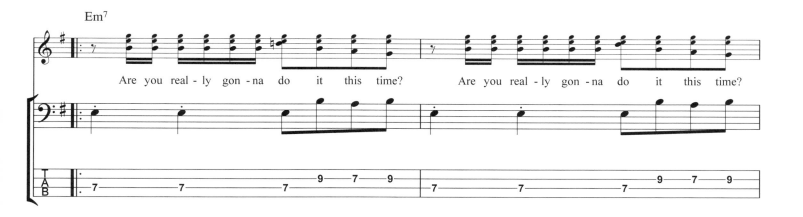

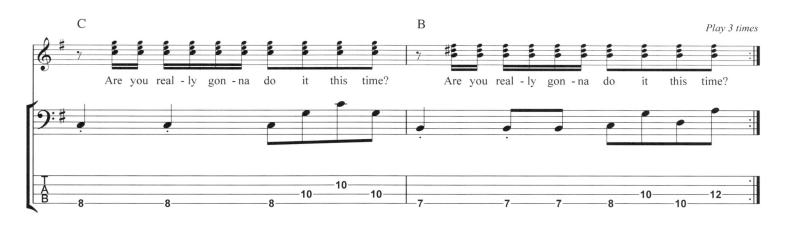

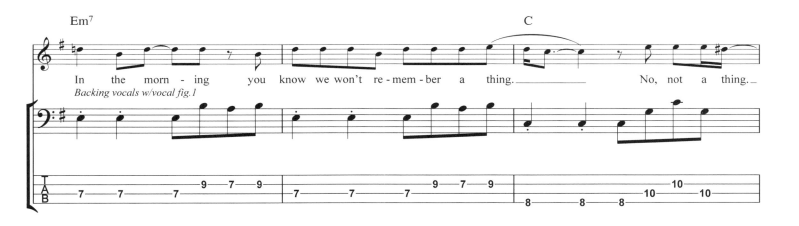

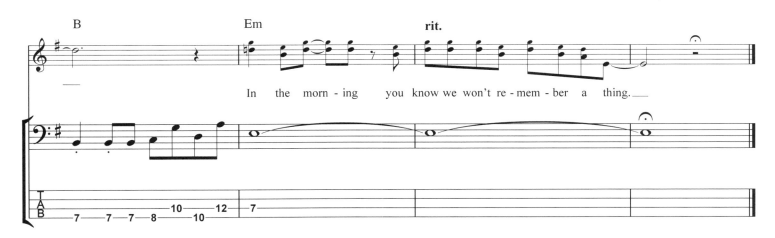

RIP IT UP

Song by Johnny Borrell
Music by Razorlight

Full performance demo: CD track 7
Backing only: CD track 15

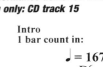

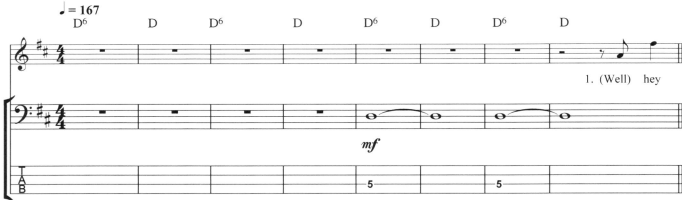

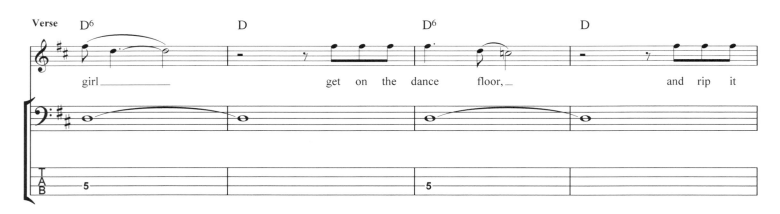

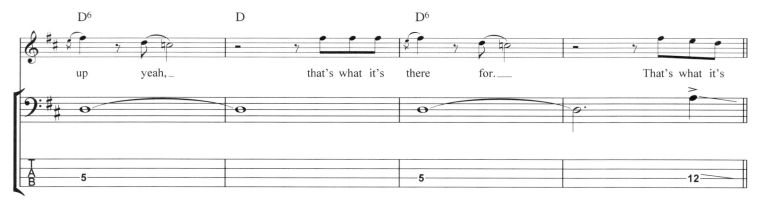

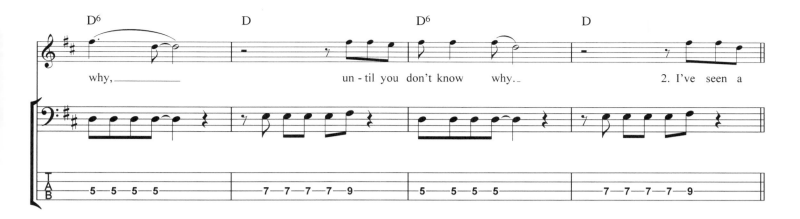

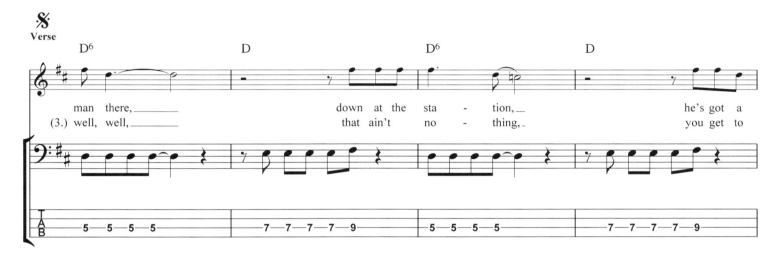

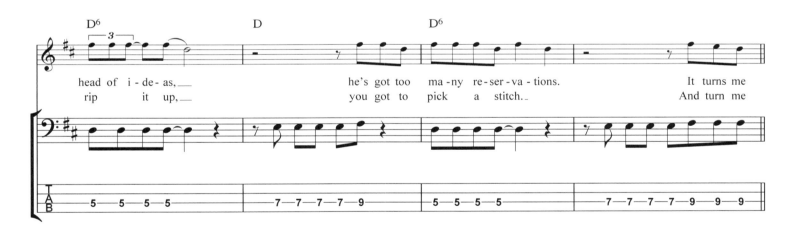

why, _____ un - til you don't know why. _
why, _____ you know I don't know why. _
She says,

Bridge

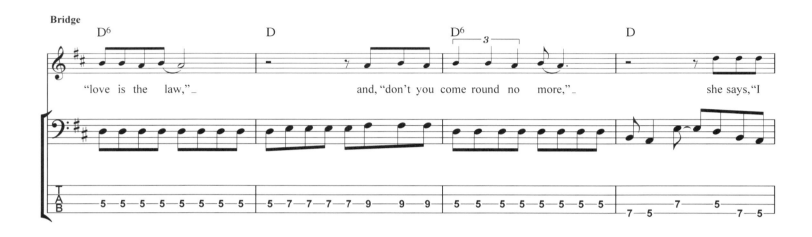

"love is the law," _ and, "don't you come round no more," _ she says, "I

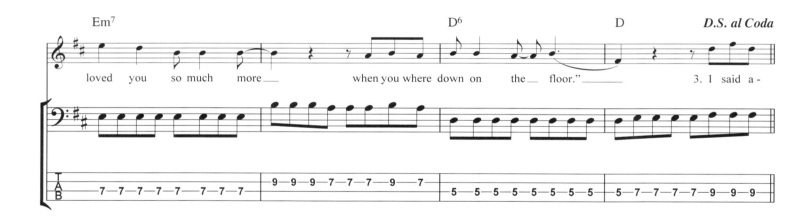

loved you so much more ___ when you where down on the _ floor." _____ 3. I said a-

D.S. al Coda

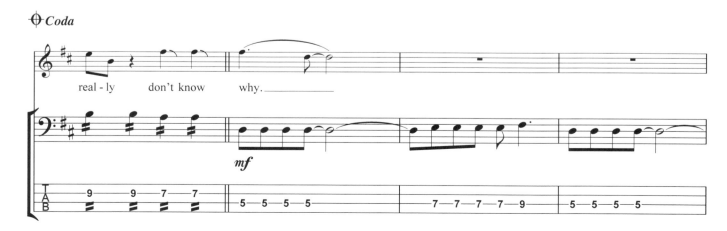

real - ly don't know why. _____

$\oplus$ *Coda*

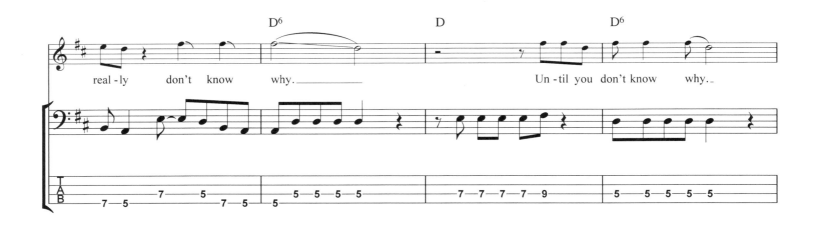

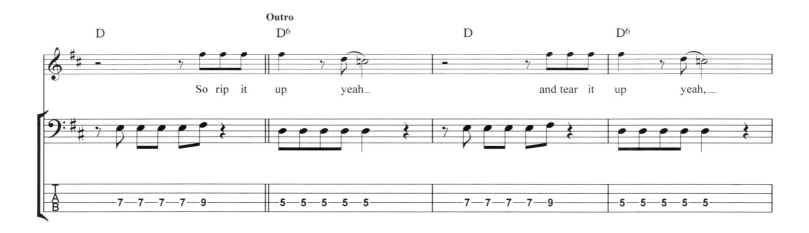

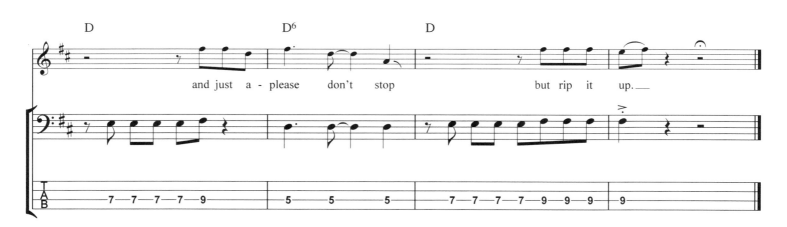

SOMEWHERE ELSE

Song by Johnny Borrell
Music by Razorlight

Full performance demo: CD track 8
Backing only: CD track 16

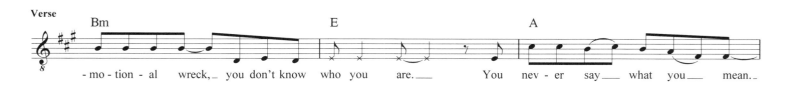

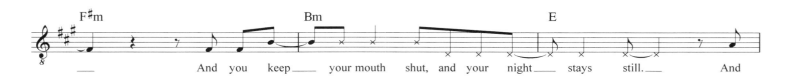

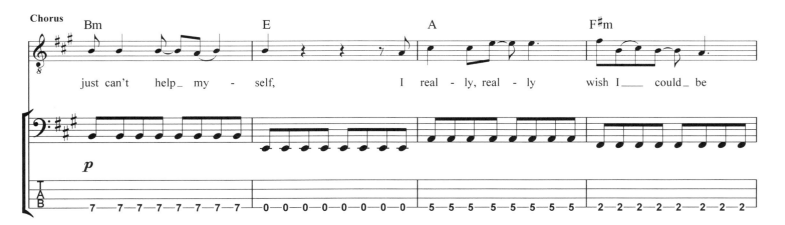

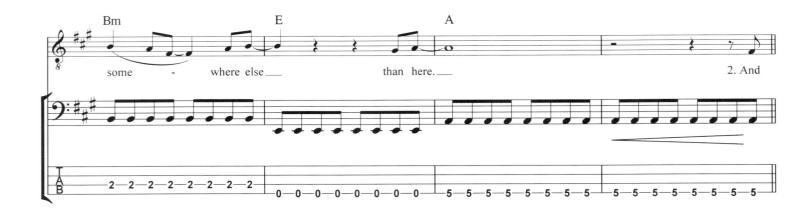

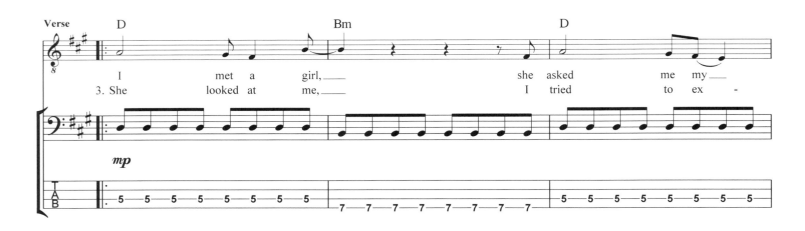

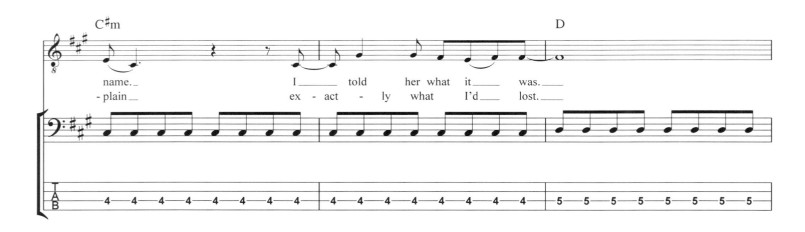

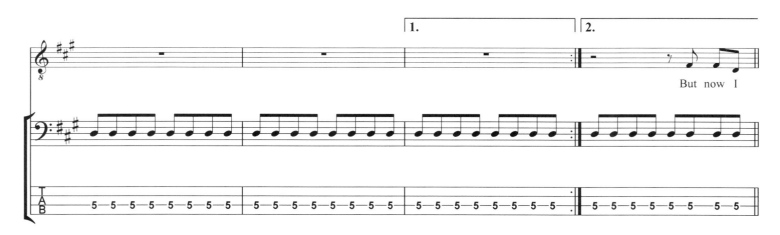

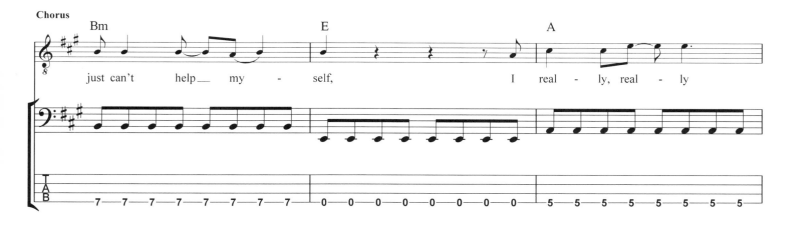

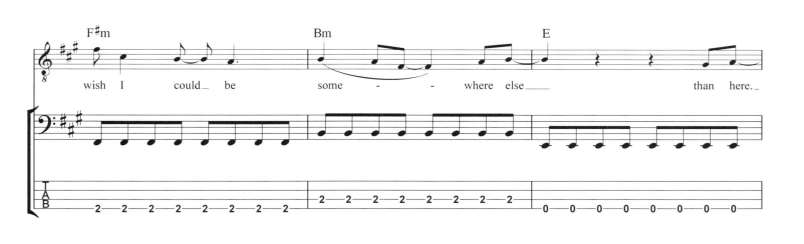

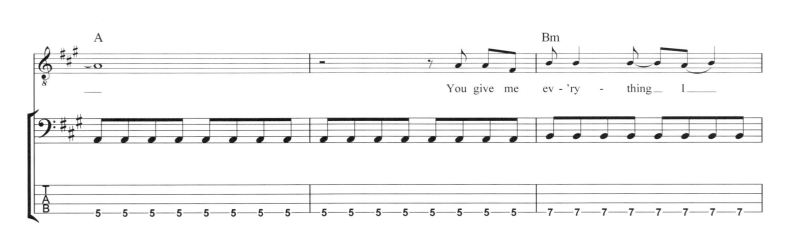

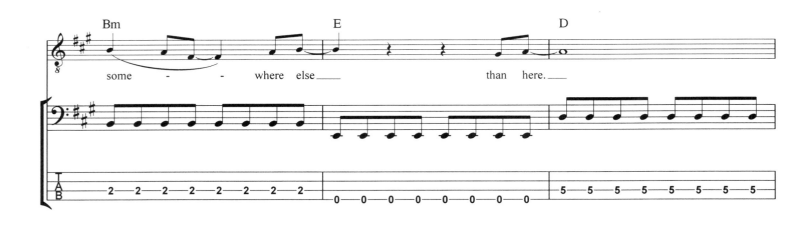

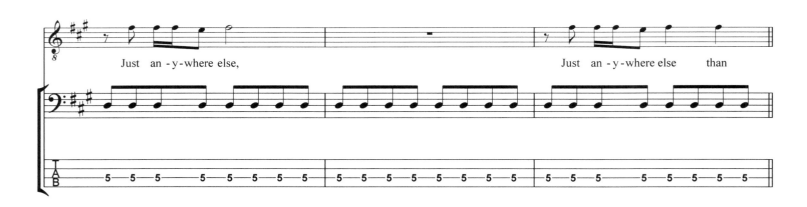

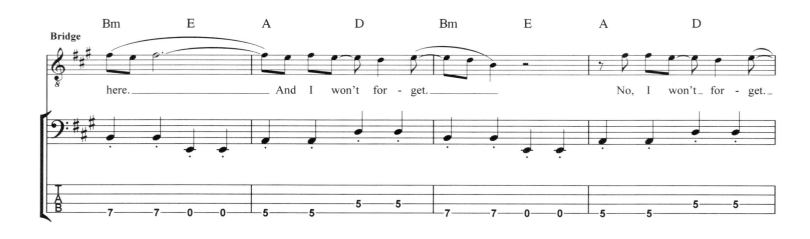

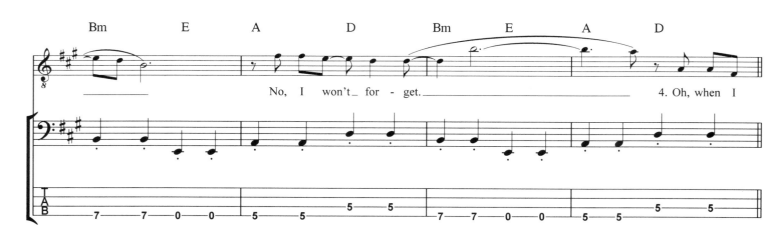

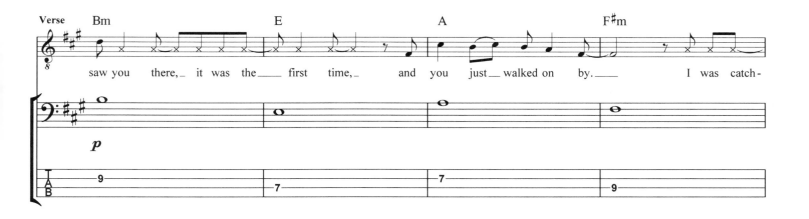

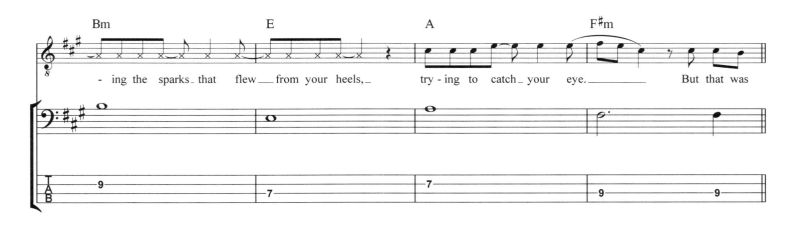

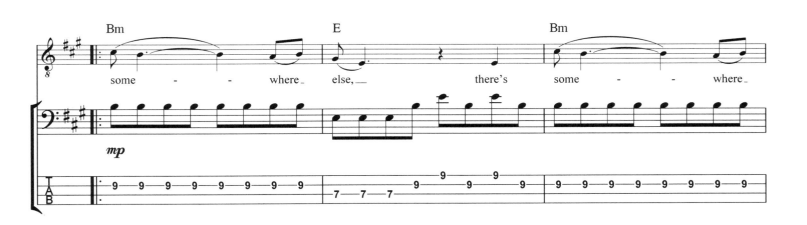

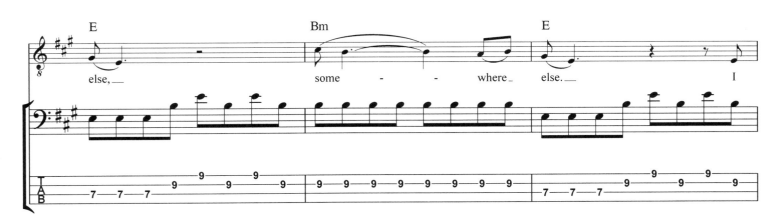

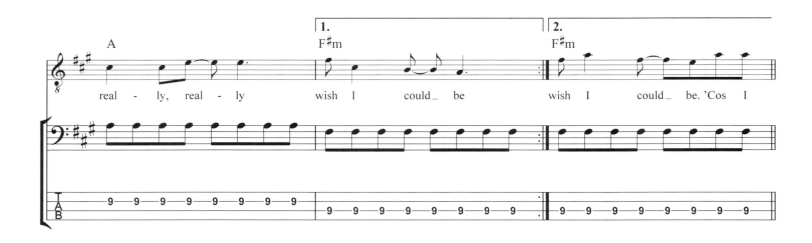

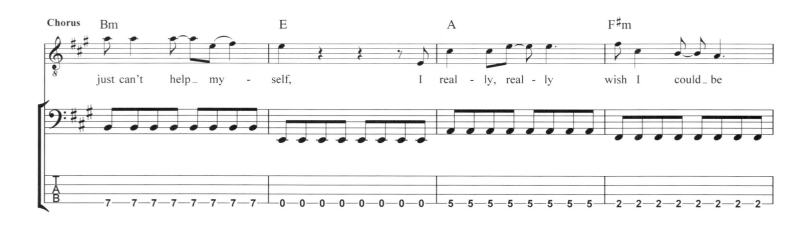

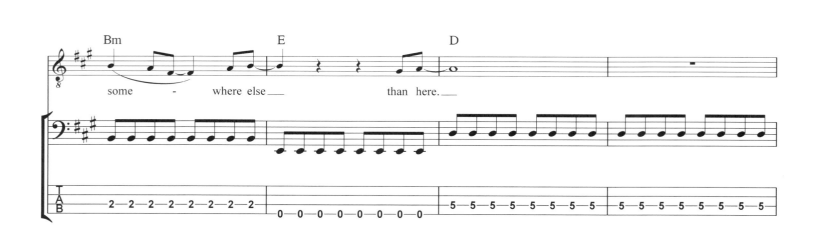

-self, I real - ly, real - ly wish I could._ I got ev -'ry - thing I need,_

_ I real - ly, real - ly wish I could_ be

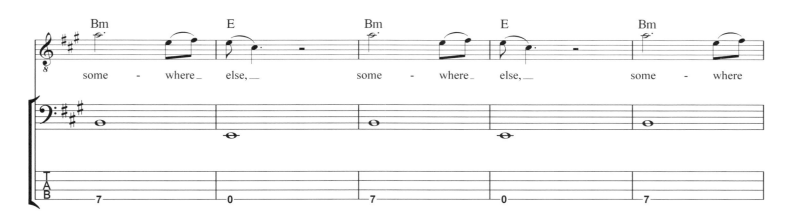

some - where_ else,_ some - where_ else,_ some - where

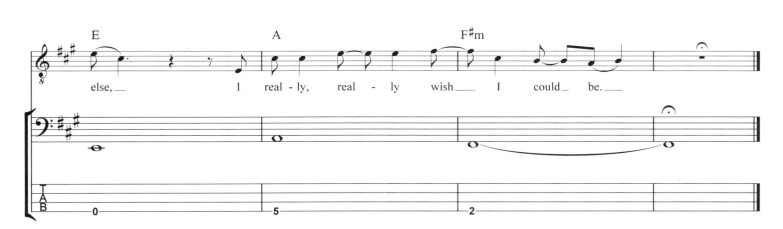

else,_ I real - ly, real - ly wish_ I could_ be._

VICE

Song by Johnny Borrell
Music by Razorlight

Full performance demo: CD track 9
Backing only: CD track 17

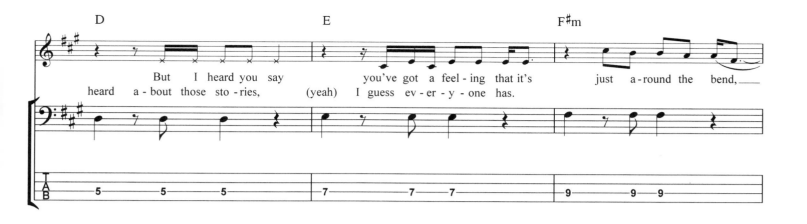

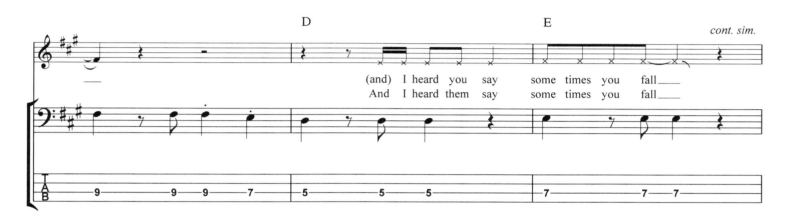

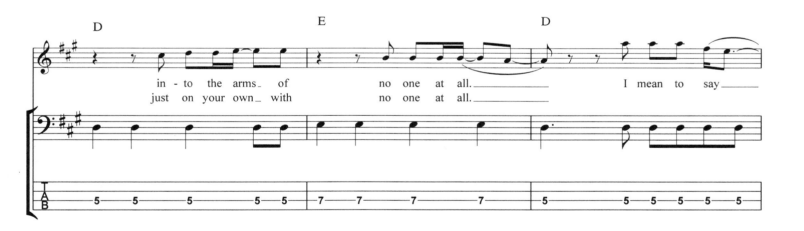

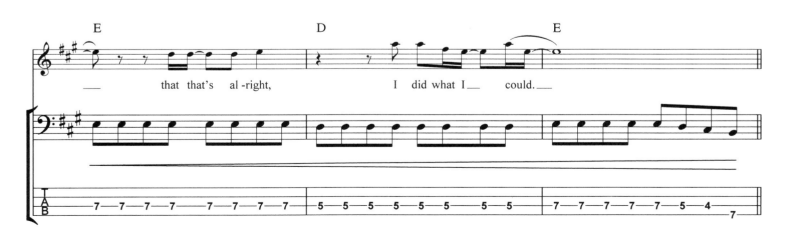

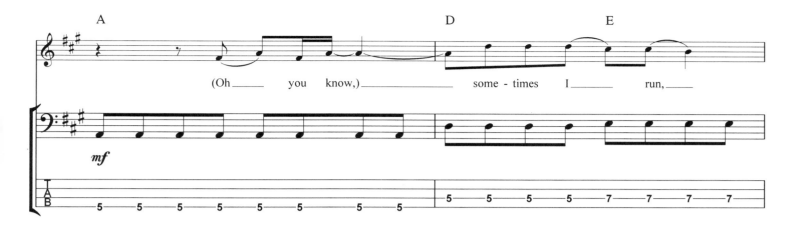

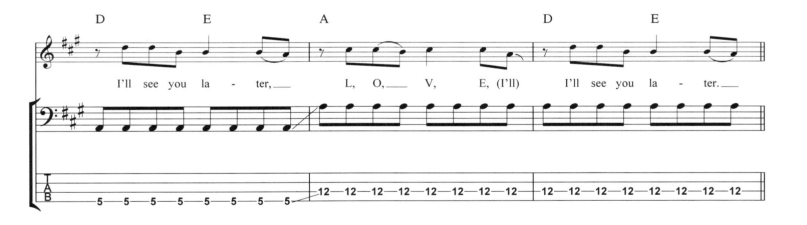

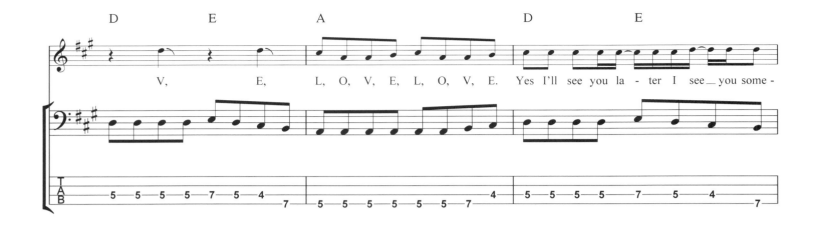

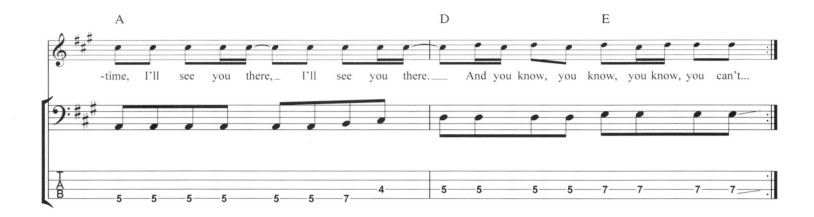

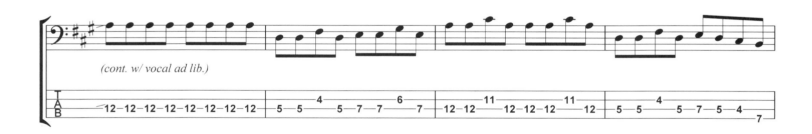

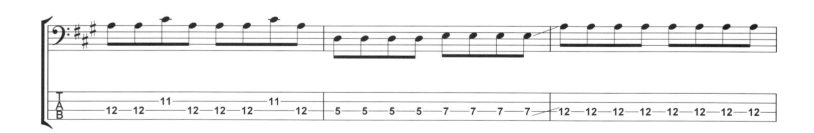

123456789

Also available in the series

play BASS with...

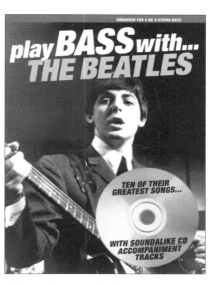

Play Bass With...
THE POLICE

Nine Great Tracks...
CAN'T STAND LOSING YOU
DON'T STAND SO CLOSE TO ME
EVERY BREATH YOU TAKE
EVERY LITTLE THING SHE DOES IS MAGIC
MESSAGE IN A BOTTLE
ROXANNE
SPIRITS IN THE MATERIAL WORLD
SYNCHRONICITY II
WALKING ON THE MOON
AM991309

Play Bass With...
THE BEATLES

Ten Great Titles...
A HARD DAY'S NIGHT
ALL MY LOVING
CAN'T BUY ME LOVE
EIGHT DAYS A WEEK
HELP!
I FEEL FINE
I SAW HER STANDING THERE
PLEASE PLEASE ME
SHE LOVES YOU
TICKET TO RIDE
NO90904

Play Bass With...
MUSE

Nine Great Rock Hits...
BLISS
HYPER MUSIC
HYSTERIA
MUSLE MUSEUM
NEW BORN
PLUG IN BABY
STOCKHOLM SYNDROME
SUNBURN
TIME IS RUNNING OUT
AM981354

Great songs with Soundalike CD accompaniment tracks

CD track listing

1 TUNING NOTES

FULL INSTRUMENTAL PERFORMANCES

(WITH BASS)...

2 AMERICA
(Borrell/Burrows/Ågren/Dalemo)
Sony/ATV Music Publishing (UK) Limited.

3 BACK TO THE START
(Borrell/Burrows/Ågren/Dalemo)
Sony/ATV Music Publishing (UK) Limited.

4 BEFORE I FALL TO PIECES
(Borrell/Burrows/Ågren/Dalemo)
Sony/ATV Music Publishing (UK) Limited.

5 GOLDEN TOUCH
(Borrell)
Sony/ATV Music Publishing (UK) Limited.

6 IN THE MORNING
(Borrell/Burrows/Ågren/Dalemo)
Sony/ATV Music Publishing (UK) Limited.

7 RIP IT UP
(Borrell)
Sony/ATV Music Publishing (UK) Limited.

8 SOMEWHERE ELSE
(Borrell)
Sony/ATV Music Publishing (UK) Limited.

9 VICE
(Borrell)
Sony/ATV Music Publishing (UK) Limited.

BACKING TRACKS ONLY (WITHOUT BASS)...

10 AMERICA
11 BACK TO THE START
12 BEFORE I FALL TO PIECES
13 GOLDEN TOUCH
14 IN THE MORNING
15 RIP IT UP
16 SOMEWHERE ELSE
17 VICE

To remove your CD from the plastic sleeve, lift the small lip to break the perforations. Replace the disc after use for convenient storage.